Preface

Every country has its own aural traditions of myth and legend, and the stories in this series come from the four corners of the earth. They will help the modern child to appreciate how happenings may be interpreted in different ways by people whose entire way of thinking may, for many reasons, be different.

The series is intended for an age range of 7 + to 11 +, with more easily understood stories in the first two books and more difficult concepts in the two later books.

Harry Stanton
Audrey Daly

Contents

WIDE RANGE

Myths and Legends
1

Harry Stanton
and Audrey Daly

Oliver & Boyd

Illustrated by Shirley Bellwood,
Pamela Goodchild, Donald Harley,
Annabel Large and Ray Mutimer

OLIVER & BOYD
Robert Stevenson House
1–3 Baxter's Place
Leith Walk
Edinburgh EH1 3BB

A Division of Longman Group Ltd

First published 1984

ISBN 0 05 003360 3

© Oliver & Boyd 1984

Set in Monophoto Plantin 14/20pt
Printed in Hong Kong by
Wing King Tong Printing Co. Ltd

About this Book

Long, long ago, before there were
any radios or televisions or books,
there were stories and storytellers.

The storytellers moved from place to
place, telling stories as they went.
They told stories of gods and fairies,
of ordinary men and women, of giants
and dwarfs, and of magic and mystery.

This book has a mixture of all these
stories. They come from different
lands and were told at different times.
Some of them are well-known, others
are almost forgotten, but all of
them are worth hearing again.

The Pedlar of Swaffham

Once, hundreds of years ago, a man called
John Chapman lived in the small town
of Swaffham in the county of Norfolk.

He was a pedlar, which meant that
he went from door to door selling
things like needles, pins and ribbons
to housewives.

One night John had a strange dream.
What happened in the dream was so
real that next morning he told his
wife about it.

"I dreamed I was in London, standing
on London Bridge, and a man told me
where to find buried treasure."

"You dream too much," said his wife crossly. "Go to work and forget about it."

That night John Chapman dreamed about buried treasure again, but he did not dare to tell his wife about it.

The next night, however, he had the same dream yet again, and this time he told his wife.

"I've had the same dream for three nights, so I'm going to London to see if it's true," he said.

His wife was very cross and upset, but she could not stop him, and later that day he set off.

It was a long journey. He had to walk most of the way, but sometimes he would meet a farmer who would let him ride on the back of his cart.

John had very little money, so he could only buy bread and cheese to eat. Sometimes he picked berries

and wild fruit that he found beside
the road, and all he had to drink
was fresh water from the streams.
At night he slept in haystacks.

He travelled for seven days, and
at last he came in sight of London.

At first he was very frightened—
London was not a bit like Swaffham!
It was full of people, all hurrying
about their business.
John had never seen so many
people before.

When he found London Bridge
he could not see the river,
because there were houses and shops
on both sides of the bridge.
From the middle of the road,

it looked just like any other
street in London.

All day long John Chapman walked
up and down London Bridge, but
nothing happened.   No one stopped
him to tell him where to find
buried treasure.

That night he slept in a dirty
shed under some old sacks.
He did not sleep very well,
and next morning he was
very cold and hungry.

For two days more he wandered
up and down London Bridge.
At last he thought,

"It's no good, it *was*

only a dream. There's no buried
treasure after all. I'll just have
to go home."

As he crossed the bridge for
the last time, on his way back
to Swaffham, a shopkeeper spoke to him.

"I've been watching you for
three days now. Why do you keep on
walking up and down the bridge?"
he asked.

John sadly shook his head.

"I don't want to tell you. You'll
only call me a fool and laugh at me,"
he replied.

"Will you tell me if I promise
not to laugh or call you a fool?"
asked the shopkeeper.

"All right," said John. "I'll tell
you. I came to London because I had
the same dream for three nights.
I dreamed that I was on London Bridge,
and a man would tell me where to
find buried treasure."

The shopkeeper did not laugh.

"That's strange," he said.
"For three nights I too have had
a dream about buried treasure.
I dreamed I went to a town in
Norfolk called Swaffham.   I don't
even know if there *is* such a town.
In *my* dream I went to a pedlar's house
and began to dig under an oak tree,
and there I found a chest full of treasure."

John Chapman could hardly believe
his ears.   *He* was a pedlar from Swaffham,
and there was an oak tree in *his* garden!

Then the shopkeeper said,

"But I don't believe in dreams,
so I'm not silly enough to go looking
for the treasure," and he went back
inside his shop.

John Chapman made his way back
to Swaffham as quickly as he could.
As soon as he got home, he found
a spade and began to dig
under the oak tree.

His wife followed him and
shouted, "What are you doing?"
but he did not reply.

"My poor husband has gone mad!"
she cried.

All his children came to watch
their father digging in the garden.
The hole got deeper and deeper,
but John Chapman kept on digging
until his spade struck something hard.

It was a wooden chest! His wife
and children helped him to pull it
out of the hole, and carry it
into the house.

When they opened it,
they found that it was
full of gold coins.

"Those dreams were right!"
said John, smiling.

"Yes, they were true," said
his wife.

John and his family were never
poor again, but he did not keep all
the money for himself.

He felt that God had been good
to him, so he gave much of it
to the church.

And even today, if you should
ever go to the church of St Paul
and St Peter in Swaffham, you will
find a carving of John Chapman,
the pedlar of Swaffham, whose
dreams came true.

The Giant and the Cobbler

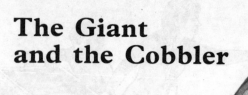

Once—long, long ago—
a young giant lived in
the mountains of Wales.
Even when he was
very young, he was so
tall that he could see
over the tops of small
mountains. His hair
was like a forest of
trees, and his voice
was like thunder.

He was a lonely young giant
because he had no one to play with.
He had no brothers or sisters,
and ordinary folk ran away and hid
when they saw him.

One day he could not think
of anything to do and the time
was passing very slowly.
For a while he threw stones
into the sea, then he went
to find his mother.

She was washing some clothes
in a lake, and making such
large waves that the fish hid
in the mud by the far shore.

"I want something to do,"
said the young giant.

"What do you want to do?"
asked his mother.

"I don't know," he said.
Then he thought for a moment.
"I know! I'd like to play a trick."

"Well, go and play a trick on
someone else," said his mother.
"I must do this washing."

"Who can I play a trick on?"
he asked.

"*I* don't know," said his mother,

as she went on doing the washing.

"But I want to play a trick
on someone!" He stamped his foot,
and made the hills shake.

His mother looked at him again.

"Why not go and play a trick
on the people of Shrewsbury?"

"Shrewsbury?" said the giant.
"Where is Shrewsbury?"

His mother pointed over the
mountains to the east.

"That way, by the River Severn,"
she said.

"I know a good trick," said
the giant. "If Shrewsbury is by
a river, I shall take a spadeful
of earth and put it across the river.
Then it will flood the town.
That will be a good trick!"

So he took his spade, dug up
a mountain and began to carry it
to Shrewsbury.

It was a long way and he kept

getting lost.   His spadeful
of mountain grew heavier and heavier.
Time after time he had to stop
and put his spade down, to rest.

Later, as it began to get dark,
the giant saw a cobbler walking
along the road.

"You!" shouted the giant.
"Is it far to Shrewsbury?"

"Shrewsbury?   Why do you want to
go to Shrewsbury?" asked the cobbler.

"I'm going to play a trick on the
people of Shrewsbury," said the giant.

"What trick are you going to play

on them?" asked the cobbler.

"I'm going to take this mountain
that I have on my spade, and put
it in the river, then the river
will flood the town of Shrewsbury,"
replied the young giant.

"Oh dear," said the cobbler.
"If you do that, the people will
have nowhere to live."

The giant nodded his head.

"And some people will be drowned,"
said the cobbler.

The young giant only smiled and
nodded his head once again.

"This is terrible," the cobbler
said to himself. "However can I
stop him?" He knew that if
Shrewsbury was flooded, there would
be no more shoes for him to mend.
He *had* to stop the giant.
He thought quickly, then he said,

"It's a long way to Shrewsbury."

"How far?" asked the giant.

"Many days' journey," replied
the cobbler. He took from his back
the sack of shoes that he was taking
home to mend, and he tipped them
out on to the road.

"Look!" he shouted up at the giant.
"Look at all these shoes that I have
worn out since I set out from Shrewsbury."

The young giant looked down at them.

"I'm not going that far," he shouted.
"I'm going back to my mother."
And he dropped the mountain from
his spade and went back to Wales.

And today, not far from Shrewsbury,
there is a hill called the Wrekin.
It is just where the giant gave up,
dropped the mountain from his spade,
and went back home!

Four Wishes

Glooscap, one of the gods of the
North American Indians, lived
a long way from the land of men
and women.

He was one of their favourite gods,
however, so each year many people made
the long journey to where he lived.
They knew that Glooscap always
welcomed people who reached his home,
and would give them anything
they asked for if it was good.

But if they asked for something
which was unwise or evil, Glooscap
would punish them.

One day four men arrived at
his wigwam.

"Please can you help me?"
asked the first man. "I have evil
thoughts and I'm often very angry.
Please help me to live in peace."

Glooscap nodded his head. He
turned to the second man and asked,

"How can I help you?"

"I'm poor because I'm so lazy,"
replied the man. "Please help me
to work harder or my children
will go hungry."

Glooscap nodded his head once again

and turned towards the third man.

"And how can I help you?" he asked.

"Nobody likes me, and I haven't
any friends," replied the man.
"People laugh at me.   Please help me
to find some friends."

Glooscap looked at the man
and nodded his head.

Then he turned to the last man
and asked him, "How can I help you?"

The man stood up and said,

"You can see that I'm tall and handsome.
I would like to be even bigger,
and to live longer than any other man
in my tribe."

Glooscap looked at the man and smiled.
Then he nodded his head.   For a few
moments the god sat thinking,
then he went into his wigwam and
brought out four tiny boxes.

He gave one to each man and said,

"Take this, but don't open it until
you are safely inside your home.

Go now, and journey safely."

The first three men hurried away
and travelled home as quickly
as possible.

As each arrived at his own wigwam,
he opened his tiny box to find
that it was filled with a sweet-smelling
ointment.   And as each one rubbed
the ointment on his body, he knew
that his wish was coming true.

The fourth man did not hurry home.
As soon as the other men were out
of sight, he stopped in the forest
and opened his tiny box.   Inside was
a sweet-smelling ointment.

He rubbed the ointment on his body
and he too could tell that his wish
had been granted. He could feel
himself growing taller and taller.
And taller and taller—changing
into a tall pine tree which lived
much longer than any of the men
in the tribe.

Stick Race

One evening, as the sun was
setting and smoke lazily drifted
from the camp fires, two children
started to shout.

"I'm better than you!"
shouted the little boy.

"No, you're not.   I'm the best!"
his sister shouted back.

"I *am* the best!" the boy
shouted again.

"No, *I'm* the best!" his sister
shouted back.

Their old grandmother hurried
from her tent and said,

"Children, children!
Stop that shouting at once!
You must never shout that you are
the best."

She made them sit down quietly,
then she told them this story.

Long, long ago, the people
of the plains used to race against
one another. Each village
had a team of runners. When
they raced, each team kicked a
stick in front of them.
The people of one village,
Eagle Village, became very good
at the stick race. They could
beat every other team, and
every time there was a race, they won.

"We're the best," they shouted.
"We're the best. We *always* win."

It was true—they always did win.
No one else could beat them, but
the other teams did not like
to hear them boasting.

"How can we stop them?" asked
people from the other villages.
They talked and talked but they
could not think what to do.

At last they all fell silent.
Then an old man spoke.

"I know who can help us," he said.
Everyone looked at the old man.

"Who?" they asked.

"My friend who lives beside
the river—old Musk Rat.   He is
wise and cunning.   I'll go
and ask him."

The next day the old man
went across the plains to where
the old Musk Rat lived.   Musk Rat
was digging a hole in the river bank.

"Greetings," said the old man.
"I've come to ask your help."

Musk Rat listened to his story,
then he said, "Yes, I'll help you.
I'll race against the young men
from Eagle Village myself.
But I must be allowed to run
the race in my own way. I must
be allowed to run underground."

The runners from Eagle Village
laughed when they heard the news.

"Of course old Musk Rat can
race against us," they said.
"We'll beat him just the same
as we beat everyone else."

"But he must be allowed to run
underground," said the old man.

"He can run any way he wants,"
said the team from Eagle Village.
"We shall still win. Tell him
we'll race him tomorrow morning."

Now Musk Rat had eight brothers
who all looked exactly like him,
and that night he went to see them.

"Brothers," he said, "I'm going

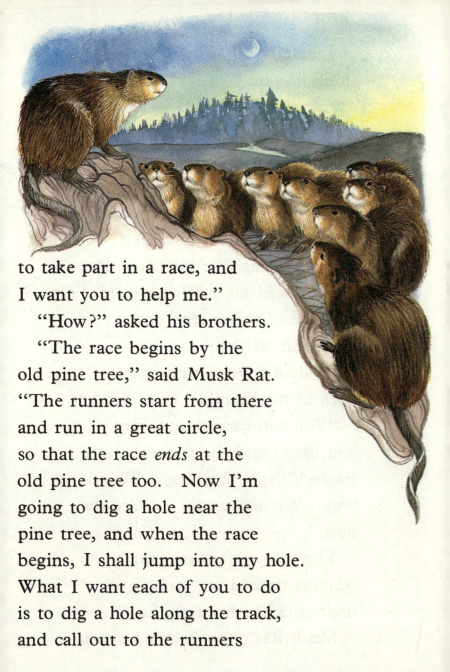

to take part in a race, and
I want you to help me."

"How?" asked his brothers.

"The race begins by the
old pine tree," said Musk Rat.
"The runners start from there
and run in a great circle,
so that the race *ends* at the
old pine tree too. Now I'm
going to dig a hole near the
pine tree, and when the race
begins, I shall jump into my hole.
What I want each of you to do
is to dig a hole along the track,
and call out to the runners

as they go past, so that they
think it's me."

His brothers began to laugh
as they saw his idea. "We'll
do that for you," they promised.

Next morning the team from
Eagle Village arrived early with
their sticks, and they waited
at the starting line for Musk Rat.

He poked his head out of his hole
near the old pine tree, and
looked up at them.

"I shall have to carry the
stick in my mouth," he told them.

"You can carry it any way
you like," said the runners from
Eagle Village, laughing. "We'll
win. We *always* do. We're the
best."

The race started and the
runners dashed off, kicking
their sticks in front of them.

Musk Rat popped into his hole

holding his stick in his mouth.
A few minutes later, the Eagle
Village team saw the first
of Musk Rat's brothers.

"Hello," he shouted, then
popped back into his hole.

"We'll have to go faster,"
shouted one of the runners.
"He is as fast as we are!"

They all ran faster, but
a little further along the track,
another of Musk Rat's brothers
popped up just in front of them.

"Can't you go any faster?"
he called back, teasing them.

The Eagle Village team were
growing worried.

"Old Musk Rat is as fast as
we are. We won't win unless
we *really* hurry!"

Each time the runners saw
another of Musk Rat's brothers,
they ran faster and faster.
At last they were running
very fast indeed.

Soon they came to the end
of the race. As they raced
for the line, Musk Rat heard
them coming. He jumped out of
the hole where he had been hiding,
and ran across the finishing line
with his stick in his mouth.
He was just ahead of the runners
from Eagle Village.

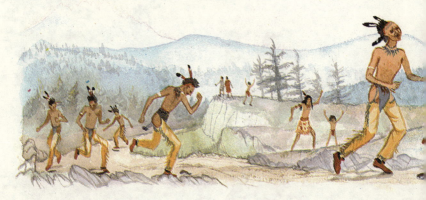

People from all the villages
around had come to watch.
As Musk Rat crossed the finishing
line, they all began to cheer.

"Well done, Musk Rat, well done!"
they shouted.   They were very
pleased that Eagle Village had
at last been beaten.

Musk Rat turned to the runners
and said, "You do look tired!"—and
everyone cheered more than ever.

From that day to this, the
runners from Eagle Village have
never shouted, "We're the best,
we *always* win."   They could never
boast again, for old Musk Rat
had beaten them.

The Man who Stayed Poor

Once upon a time, in the land
of Ghana, there lived a poor man
who worked for a farmer.

He was so very poor that
he complained about it every
single day.   He complained
so much that at last
the king himself heard about it.
He sent for the man and asked,

"Why are you always complaining?"
The poor man bowed low.

"I complain because no matter
how hard I work, I never earn
any extra money. And I know
that as long as I live,
I shall *always* be poor,"
said the man.

"If you are honest, you will
become rich," said the king.

"But I *am* honest,"
replied the man.

For a moment or two the king
sat and looked at him
in silence, then he said,

"I'm going to give you
two presents. The little one
is for you, and the big one is for
the farmer for whom you work."

The poor man was pleased
as the king gave him two sacks—
a big one and a little one.

"Now don't forget," said the king,
as the man set off for home,
"the little sack is for you,

and the big sack is for
the farmer for whom you work."

The poor man walked along
quickly at first, still pleased
with his present.

After a while, he sat down
to rest.   He put the two sacks
where he could see them,
and he began to think,

"Why did the king give the farmer
the big sack?   I'm much poorer than
he is."

And as he walked on,
he said to himself,

"Since no one else knows that
the big sack is for the farmer,
I could give him the little one
and keep the big one for myself."

Then he shook his head.

"No, no, that wouldn't be honest,"
he said to himself, and he
walked on quickly.

At last, when he was not far

from home, the poor man began
to walk more and more slowly.
Then he hid the big sack
behind a tree, and took
the little one to the farmer.

The farmer was very pleased
to get a present from the king,
and he opened it at once.
It was full of gold!

The poor man couldn't
believe his eyes. He ran back
to where he had hidden
the big sack, and as he ran
he kept shouting,

"I'm rich!   I'm rich!"
But when he opened the sack,
it was full of seed.

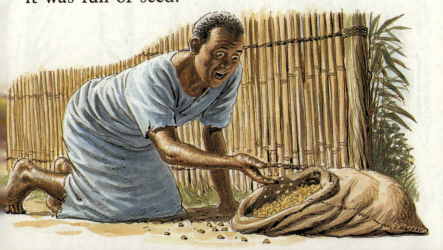

The Greedy Boy

Long, long ago, in the land
of India, a holy man lived
in a temple.

Now the holy man was quite old,
so he had a boy to help him
to look after the temple.
The boy was supposed to help
to get the holy man's food ready too,
but he was very lazy—
and very, very greedy.

One day the holy man sent him
out to beg for food.   The boy
took a basket and he went
to the village.

He called at each house,
and sometimes he was given
one pie, and sometimes two pies.
At last the basket was full,
and he sat down and began
to count the pies.

He had thirty-two!

"Thirty-two pies," he said
to himself, licking his lips.
"My master is a kind man,
and when I get back, I know
he'll give me half of them."

Then he tried to work out
how many he would get.

"One for me," he said, putting
a pie on one side of him.
"One for my master," and he
put a pie at the other side.
"Another one for me—

and another one for my master."

He went on like this until
he had shared out all the pies.
Then he counted both piles.

"Sixteen for me, and sixteen
for my master!" he said, pleased.

He looked at the pies
for a moment.

"Thirty-two pies," he said
to himself again, slowly.
"My master is sure to give
me half of them.
So he won't mind if I eat

my half now, because I'm hungry."

Then, one after the other, he ate the pile of sixteen pies. When he had finished he put the others back in the basket.

As he was walking back to the temple, he counted the pies again.

"Sixteen pies!" he said to himself. "My master is a kind man. He does not eat very much and I know he will give me half of them when I get back."

Once again he set the pies into two piles.

"One for me, and one for my master," he said, as he counted them out.

When he had shared them out, he found that he had eight pies in each pile.

He looked at them for a moment.

"My master would have given me half of them," he said to himself—and he ate another eight pies.

Then, as he walked along the road to the temple, he began to count the pies again.

"There are eight pies here," he said. "My master is a kind man and he is sure to give me half of them."

He stopped and put down his basket, and once more he counted out the pies into two piles.

He looked at them, then he said to himself,

"As my master will give me four pies and I'm still hungry, I will eat them now."
So he ate them.

He put the other four pies

back in the basket, and
slowly walked along the road
towards the temple.   As he
walked, he looked at the four
pies that he had left.

"There are not many pies here,"
he said to himself.   "There are only four.
I know my master will share
them with me.   He will have two and
I will have two.   So I'll eat them now."

He ate the two pies—and then
another one!

Now there was only one pie left.
He looked at it and said,

"There is only one pie here.
My master is sure to give me half of it."
So he ate half of it.

At last he arrived back at the
temple.   The holy man, his master,
looked in the basket and said,
"Is that all the people of the village
gave you?"
The greedy boy did not dare to
tell a lie.   He told his master
how he had eaten one pie after another.
"You greedy boy!" shouted his master.
"How did you manage to eat so many pies?"
"Like this," said the greedy boy.
He reached out, took the last piece of
pie, and swallowed it.
What do *you* think happened next?

The Inn
of Donkeys

As a merchant rode along
a lonely road in the north
of China, he looked for somewhere
to stay the night.   It was
growing dark, and he felt tired
and hungry.

He saw a man working
in a field, and asked,

"Can you tell me where I can
stay the night?"

"The Wooden Bridge Inn just
over the hill is very good,"
replied the man,

"and the lady who keeps the Inn
also sells very good donkeys.
She is rich, so she sells them
very cheaply."

"Where does she get the
donkeys from?" asked the merchant.

"I don't know," said the man,
turning back to his work.

The merchant went on his way,
and soon he came to the
Wooden Bridge Inn. He left
his donkey in the stable and
went inside.

Five other travellers were
also staying the night.
The lady of the Inn made them
a fine dinner of chicken, fish and rice.

Afterwards she gave them wine,
and they sat talking and drinking.

The merchant did not have any
wine, because he did not like it,
but he sat and talked
to the other travellers until
it was time for bed.

Soon the Inn was quiet,
for the wine made everyone
fall asleep very quickly.

The merchant lay awake,
however, and suddenly, in the
darkness, he heard a strange
scraping noise. As the noise
grew louder, he began to wonder
what it could be.

He got out of bed quietly, and
went to peep into the next room.
The lady of the Inn
was dragging a large black box
into her room.

As the merchant watched, she
opened the lid, reached in and

took out a tiny wooden man
no bigger than her hand.

She reached into the box again,
and this time she brought out
a tiny wooden ox and a plough.
She fixed the ox to the plough,
then put the man behind the plough.

Lastly, she took a small jug
of water and sprinkled
water over them.

As soon as the water touched
them, the ox started to move,
pulling the plough, and the man
walked along behind.

The floor of the room was made
of earth, and the ox ploughed it up.

The lady of the Inn then gave
the tiny man some seed.
He planted it and it began to grow.

At first it was green, but
it ripened quickly. Then the
lady took the plants and rubbed
the grain from them. She took
two round stones from inside
the box, placed the grain between
them and ground it into flour.
With the flour, she made some
cakes which she baked in the oven.

Before she could turn round
and see him, the merchant went
back to bed and lay awake for
the rest of the night,
thinking about what he had seen.

Next morning the lady of the
Inn served breakfast to her guests.
She gave them the cakes she
had made in the night.

The merchant did not eat
his cake. Instead he hid it
in his coat, and went out to
feed his donkey.

As he left the room, he
heard a strange noise.
He looked back and saw the other
guests fall to the floor.
Their clothes began to change
into grey hairy coats.
They grew tails and long ears.
They had changed into donkeys!

The merchant was very frightened.

Quickly he took his donkey
from the stable and hurried away.

He was too frightened to tell
anyone about what he had seen.
Besides, he thought
people would not believe him.

A week later, on his way home,
the merchant bought some cakes
that looked just like the ones
that the lady of the Inn
had made.

When he came to the Wooden
Bridge Inn, he stayed the night,
just as he had before.

Everything happened just as
it had happened the first time.

Once again, when all the guests
had gone to bed, he heard the
lady of the Inn drag her black
box across the room.
He got out of bed quietly,
and went to see what was happening.

And, just as before, she

took the tiny wooden man, the
ox and the plough from the box.
After she had sprinkled water
on them, they began to plough up
the floor. Then the man planted
the seeds, which quickly grew
into plants with grain on them.

The merchant smiled to himself
as he saw the lady of the Inn
grind the grain into flour
to make cakes for breakfast.

Next morning, when the lady
of the Inn brought the merchant
his breakfast, with some of
her cakes, she found that he
had already set the table.
On it were the cakes he had
brought with him.

"Come and have one of *my*
cakes for breakfast," he said.

Then, when she was not looking,
he changed the cakes over—
and gave her one of her own cakes!

"Your cakes are very nice,"
she said as she ate it.
She reached out to take another
one, but before she could pick
it up, she fell to the ground.

Her clothes began to change
into a grey hairy coat, and
slowly she grew a grey tail
and long ears.

The lady of the Inn had
changed into a donkey!
And she was such a fine, strong
donkey that the merchant rode
away upon her—after he had
had his breakfast.

The San Antonio Vine

One Christmas Eve in the San
Antonio Valley in Texas, a poor
Indian boy sat in the shade of a tree.
He was watching other people
take their gifts into church, and
wondering how he could find or make
a suitable gift.

He had no money at all,
and he owned nothing of any value.

As the day drew to a close,
he felt so sad that he began
to cry.

Suddenly a kind voice asked,
"What's the matter?"
The boy looked up to see the old
priest beside him.

"I have nothing to give
the Christ child," he cried.
"I have no money, and the clothes
I'm wearing are the only things
I own."

"Don't worry," said the old priest,
smiling. "We only give presents
to show our love of God.
How much they cost isn't important."

For a while, the poor Indian boy
did not understand
what the priest had said.
Then he noticed a tiny vine
growing between two stones.
Very carefully he dug it up and
carried it home.

He found a small jar in the kitchen
and he planted the vine in it.

He waited near the church
until nobody was about, then he took in
his simple little present.

Some of the gifts had cost
a lot of money.
They were so beautiful
that the boy felt ashamed of his
own poor gift.
He placed it behind the manger
where no one could see it.

When daybreak came on Christmas
morning, the bells began to ring.
Soon the streets were full of people
on their way to church.
The poor Indian boy went too.

Suddenly he heard a shout from
the church.

"Miracle! It's a miracle!"

He pushed his way through the
crowds round the manger,
and tears of joy came to his eyes.
The little vine had grown
during the night, and it had

twined itself around the manger
and the Christ child.

The bright green leaves and
scarlet berries made the poor Indian
boy's present the most beautiful gift
of all.

The vine still grows in the
San Antonio Valley, and ever since
that day, it is a favourite Christmas
decoration among the Indians.

Trajan's Ears

Many hundreds of years ago, there lived a ruler called Trajan. He was rich and powerful. He had a vast empire, he lived in a beautiful palace, and he had a huge army. But in spite of all these things, Trajan was not happy.

He was unhappy because he had a strange secret that he did not want anyone else to know. He did not want other people to know that his ears were long and pointed, and covered with grey hairs. They were just like a goat's ears!

Trajan was famous for his hats, for no one ever saw him without a hat which covered his ears. He wore a different one every day—sometimes made of silk, sometimes of wool, and sometimes even of fur.

When visitors from other lands
came to see Trajan, they always brought
him a hat as a present.

The only people who ever discovered
that Trajan had goat's ears were
the barbers who cut his hair.

Each time that a new barber came
to the palace, Trajan would ask,

"What did you see when you cut my hair?"

"Your ears, my lord, your beautiful
ears," each barber would reply.

And every time this happened,
Trajan had the barber locked away
in the dungeons beneath the palace,
so that he could not tell anyone else
about the strange ears.

No barber who went to the palace
was ever seen again.

After a while people began to ask
about the barbers who went to the palace
but no one could find out what had
happened to them. Soon every barber
in the land began to dread the day
when he would be asked to cut
the king's hair.

Late one evening, a messenger
arrived at the house of a barber
who lived in a tiny village
a long way from the palace.

Next morning the barber pretended
to be too ill to travel to the palace.
He called his young apprentice to him.

"You must go to the palace
in my place. I'm too ill," said the barber.

So the apprentice packed his bag
and slowly made his way to the palace.

Trajan looked at the apprentice
and said,

"Are you the barber?
You look very young."

"My master is sick, so he sent me,"
replied the apprentice.

Trajan sat down on a chair
and told the apprentice to begin.
Carefully he took off Trajan's hat,
and the first things he saw
were the long pointed ears.

As soon as he saw them,
the boy knew why the other
barbers had never been seen again.
Trajan was afraid that all
the people in the land would learn
his secret and laugh at him.

"What do you see?" asked Trajan.

"I can see that your hair is
very long and needs cutting,"
said the boy, trembling.

"What else?" asked Trajan.

"I can see it is very beautiful
hair," said the young apprentice.

Very carefully, he combed and cut
Trajan's hair. When he had finished,
Trajan asked him again what he had seen.

"All I can see, sir, is that you
have the most beautiful hair in the
whole country," replied the boy.

Trajan was very pleased with the
boy's answer. He gave him ten pieces
of gold and told him to come back
to the palace the next week.

"From now on, you shall always
be my barber and cut my hair,"
said Trajan as the boy left the palace.

The boy's master was very surprised
to see him return home.

"Tell me, what happened at the
palace?" asked the barber.

"Trajan sat in a chair and I cut
his hair," replied the apprentice.

The barber asked many more questions.
The boy answered all of them—
but he never told him that Trajan
had goat's ears.

From that time onwards, the young
barber went to the palace once a week
to cut Trajan's hair. He never told
anyone about Trajan's ears, but he began
to worry about the secret that he knew.

Every day he worried more and more.
At last he went to his mother.

"What shall I do?" he asked her.
"I have a secret that I dare not tell
anyone, or I shall die."

"If you cannot tell anyone,
there is only one thing you can do,"
his mother told him. "Go into the
country and dig a deep hole.
Whisper your secret into the hole
three times, then fill the hole in.
Your secret will be safely buried
there."

The boy did just as his mother
had told him. He took a spade
and went into the country where
he dug a hole. Then he whispered
"Trajan has goat's ears" three times
into the deep hole.

The boy looked round, but there was
no one who could have heard him.
After filling in the hole,
he went home, feeling much happier.

The next spring, an elder tree grew
in the soft earth where the boy
had dug the hole and told his secret.

By summer, the elder tree was quite
big. Some little boys cut off

one of its hollow stalks to make
whistles.

When they blew their whistles, they
heard voices shouting, "Trajan has
goat's ears! Trajan has goat's ears!"

All day long the boys blew their
whistles. By nightfall, everyone
in the town where they lived knew
about Trajan's ears.

Soon everybody in the land knew—
and Trajan heard about it.

He sent for the young barber.

"Why have you told everyone about
my ears?" cried Trajan.

"I have told no one," answered the boy.
"All I did was to dig a hole
and tell my secret to the ground."

"You shall die if you have
told me lies," cried Trajan.

"Sir, I believe him," said one
of Trajan's servants.
"I too heard about your ears,
but a talking whistle told me."

"A talking whistle!" shouted
Trajan in astonishment.

"Yes, it was made from an elder
bush," said the servant.

"Then we'll go and see this bush,"
said Trajan.

They went to the place where
the young apprentice had dug the hole.

Trajan ordered one of his servants
to cut off a stalk from the elder tree
that was growing there and make a whistle.

When it was finished, Trajan ordered
the servant to blow the whistle.
As soon as the whistle was blown,
a voice said, "Trajan has goat's ears."

Trajan turned to the young barber.

"You have been telling me the truth.
You shall not die."

From that time onwards, everyone
knew about Trajan's ears, and never
again did any barbers disappear into
the dungeons below the palace.

The Famous Bell of Atri

Hidden in the mountains, far
from anywhere, you will find the
small city of Atri. It is a happy
place to live, because the people
there are all very kind.

They never say or do anything
to hurt anyone else.
This story will tell just how kind
they could be.

Hundreds and hundreds of years
ago, a lofty tower was built in the
market square by order of the king
of Atri. A bell was hung in it,
with a long rope to reach down to
the ground.

When the bell was hung in the
tower, the king made a great speech.

"This is a special bell," he said.
"It has a long rope so that everyone,
however small, can reach it.

But I hope it won't be used
too often, because I only want
people to ring it if they feel that
some wrong has been done to them."

The people listened and smiled
to themselves. They knew that the
bell would not be used very often.
They were hardly ever unkind to anyone.

The bell was only used once that
year. During the following year,
it was used only twice.

After some years had passed and
the bell was never used, the mayor
of the city saw that the long rope
was getting frayed.

"We must get a new rope," he
said to himself, and he went to see
the king.

"But where can we get a new rope
from?" asked the king. "That rope
was specially made by a man who lives
on the other side of the mountains."

"We must send someone to get a new
rope from him then," said the mayor.
"But what will happen if someone wants
to ring the bell in the meantime?
That rope we have now will just break."

The king sat and thought for a while.
Then he said,

"I know. In my garden there are
some very long grape vines.
I'll get my gardener to fix one of
them to the bell, and perhaps it
will last until we can get a new rope."

So he sent for his gardener, who
found a very long grape vine and
fixed it to the bell.

"That should be all right for a
while," thought the king, looking at it.
But he reckoned without the general's
horse.

Not far from the city lived a rich
old man who had once been a general
in the king's army. He still had his
war horse, but it was growing too old
and too weak to carry him.

He looked at it one morning and
said crossly,

"I'm not going to feed
such a useless old horse any more!"
And he opened the door of the stable
and pushed the horse out into the street.

"Off you go!" he shouted, as he
slammed the door.

The old horse stood still for a
moment, wondering which way to go.
Then he limped sadly along the road.

There was very little for him to
eat, for the hot summer sun had long
since dried up the few tufts of grass
which grew beside the road.
Away from the road,
on the rocky mountains,
there were only a few small bushes
without leaves.
Whichever way he went,
he was going to be hungry.

At night it was worse, for the
poor old horse shivered in the night
air. He was cold as well as hungry.
As the days went by, he grew thinner
and thinner, and sadder and sadder,
but he plodded on.

Early one morning he came to the
city of Atri with its lofty tower
in the market place.
There was no one about as he limped
along the streets.

He stopped to drink at a fountain.
Then, as he raised his head, he saw

the green leaves on the grape vine
which was tied to the great bell.

He hobbled across and began to eat
the green leaves hungrily. And as
he tugged the leaves from the vine,
the great bell began to swing, and
then it suddenly pealed, "Ding, dong,
ding, dong." But the old horse was
so hungry, he took no notice.

The sound of the bell so early in
the morning woke everyone up.
They looked out of their windows
to see what was happening, and were
very surprised indeed.

There was a bony old horse pulling
the grape vine as he ate the leaves!

The mayor ran out from his house
and cried,

"That horse belongs to the
general, doesn't it? What is it
doing here?"

"He must have sent it away because
it is too old to work," said another
man who had hurried across the square.

"Look how hungry the poor animal
is," cried an old woman, coming to
look at him. And she went to her
house to fetch the horse a basketful
of apples to eat.

The noise grew and grew, and soon
there was such a great commotion
that the king himself hurried from
his palace into the square.

When he saw the old horse, the
king was very angry.

"This horse belongs to the old general.
Tell him that I want to see him

at once!" he ordered.

A soldier was sent to fetch the old general, who came straight away.

The king pointed sternly at the horse, and the old general hung his head.

"I should not have sent my old horse away," he said. "I am very ashamed."

"So you should be!" cried the king. "You have done him a great wrong. This animal served you with all his heart in the past. Now he is old, you must look after him, and see that he is kept warm and dry and well fed for the rest of his life."

The people of Atri clapped and cheered when the king had finished speaking.

"I will look after him," promised the general, and he took the old horse back to his stable, where he lived happily for many more years.

From that day to this, the great bell of Atri has never rung again. The people of Atri are still being kind to each other—and to their animals!

The Boy who Cried Wolf

Once upon a time, in a little
village near a mountain, there lived
a shepherd boy. Every morning,
when the sun rose, he had to take
all the sheep of the village to
the mountainside.

All day long the sheep would feed
on the grass, and the boy watched to
keep them safe from harm.

Then each evening, as the sun was
setting, he took them back to the
village.

Day after day the boy took the sheep
up the mountainside, and every day
was the same as the one before.
Then one day, he played a trick on
the people of the village.
When all was quiet, he shouted,
"Help, help, a wolf!"
The men of the village heard him.

They ran from the fields where they
were working, to help him.

Up the mountainside they ran,
hurrying as fast as they could.
But when they found the boy,
he was laughing.

"I fooled you, I fooled you,"
he said, laughing at them as they
ran up to him.

"Where is the wolf?" asked the men.

"There isn't any wolf," the boy
laughed. "But didn't I make you run!"

The men of the village were very

angry as they went back to their work.

Later that day the boy shouted,
"Help, help! There's a wolf!
Help, help! A wolf!"

The men of the village left their
fields once more and hurried up the
mountainside to his help. And once
more the boy was laughing.

"I fooled you, I fooled you!"
laughed the shepherd boy.
He thought it was a very good trick.

The men of the village did not laugh.
They were very angry as they
walked back to their fields.

At last evening came, and just
as the sun was sinking in the west,
a wolf came over the mountain.

The shepherd boy saw it as it ran
towards his sheep.

"Wolf! Wolf! Help!" he cried
at the top of his voice.

The men of the village heard him,
and they laughed.

"He's just trying to fool us again,"
they said, and got on with their work.

Later that evening, when the shepherd
boy did not come down the mountain
with the sheep, the men went to find him.

But the wolf had eaten him up.

Echo and Narcissus

Have you ever seen a narcissus?
It is a beautiful flower
which blooms in the spring,
when the daffodils are out.
Long ago, Greek storytellers
used to tell this story
about the first narcissus.

    *   *   *   *   *   *

Once upon a time, a fairy
called Echo lived in the mountains.
She was a very pretty fairy,
but she was a real chatterbox.

All day long—and sometimes all
through the night too—she
chattered and chattered and chattered.
Everyone grew tired of her, and at last
someone put a magic spell on her.
This spell made her invisible,
and it stopped her chattering.
Now, all she could ever do
was to repeat the last words
that other people said.

Poor Echo! She was really unhappy.
She could no longer chatter
to her friends. No one
wanted to talk to someone they
could not see, or hear words
they had already said themselves.
When she repeated their words,
even her best friends grew cross
with her!

Sadly she wandered across
the hills, all by herself.
She only spoke when she happened
to hear someone's voice, and

then she only repeated
the last few words she heard.

For many months she wandered
by herself, growing more and
more unhappy, until one day
she saw a young man. He was
lost, and he was striding across
the mountainside, looking for
his friends.

The young man was called
Narcissus. He was tall and very
good-looking, but he was not
a very nice person. He only
thought about what *he* wanted, and
he did not care for anyone else at all.

Echo did not know that Narcissus
was like that. She began
to follow him, and after a while
she fell in love with him.

Hour after hour Echo followed
him, but of course Narcissus could not
see her, so he did not even know
that she was there.

Each time he came to the top
of a hill, he shouted, "Hello!"
hoping that his friends
would hear him.

And each time, Echo repeated,
"Hello!"

"Someone must be near by,"
Narcissus said to himself at last.
He called out, "Where are you?"

And Echo—poor Echo!—
repeated, "Where are you?"

Narcissus looked towards her,
but of course he could not see her.

He ran down the hillside
towards the place from which
he thought Echo's voice came,
and called out, "I'm here."

"I'm here," repeated Echo,
growing more and more unhappy.

Now Narcissus thought the voice
was behind him. He turned
round and shouted once again,

"Who are you? Why do you
run away?"

"Run away," said Echo.

Narcissus grew angry. He
was sure someone was making fun
of him, and he turned and
stamped away down the hillside.

Now it was getting late
in the day. The sun was setting
and the tall trees cast long
shadows. Narcissus was tired,
hungry and thirsty—and very
annoyed with the voice
that seemed to be teasing him.

At last he came to a pool
and knelt down to drink the cool
water. And there, in the water,
he saw the most beautiful face
that he had ever seen,
looking up at him.

It was his reflection,
which he was seeing for the
very first time. For a while
he gazed and gazed, without
speaking. He was so quiet
that Echo crept up to the pool
to see what he was looking at.

At last Narcissus spoke
to the face in the water.

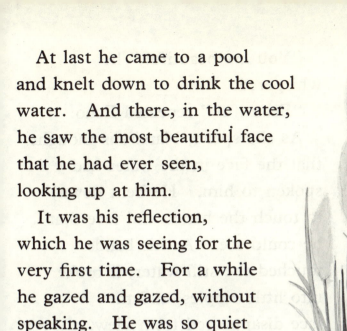

"You *are* beautiful," he whispered.

"Beautiful," repeated Echo.

As she spoke, Narcissus thought that the face in the water had spoken to him. He bent down, to touch the hands and face that he could see. As his hands touched the still water, it broke into little ripples, and the face disappeared from view.

Narcissus was very upset.

He had never seen such a lovely
face before, and now it had gone.

He waited quietly, with tears
in his eyes, then as the ripples
grew still, his reflection
looked back at him once more.

His tears dried and he smiled—
and the face in the pool smiled
back! He was so pleased that
he reached down to touch
his reflection again, and once again
it disappeared. He waited
a little while, and back it came.

And every time he tried to
touch the beautiful face in the
water, the same thing happened.

Now Narcissus was very unhappy,
just like Echo. He too was in love
for the first time in his life,
and he too could not get near
or touch the one he loved.

He cried bitterly, and the face
in the water cried too.

"Please love me!" said Narcissus.

"Please love me!" said Echo.

Each time Echo spoke,
Narcissus thought the voice
was coming from the pool.
Each time he said, "I love you,"
to his reflection, Echo repeated
his words.

Poor Echo. She had fallen
in love with Narcissus, but he
could not see her, and she
could not talk to him.
She could only repeat the
last few words that he spoke.

Narcissus stayed by the pool,
looking at the most beautiful
face that he had ever seen,
the face that he loved.

When night time came, his
reflection disappeared. He
waited for the dawn when he
would see his loved one again,
and all night long he

whispered soft words of love.
Echo repeated them sadly.

Day after day, Narcissus
sat by the pool, watching and
talking to his reflection.
He had no food, and he grew
pale and weak. At last
he died beside the pool,
looking down at his love.

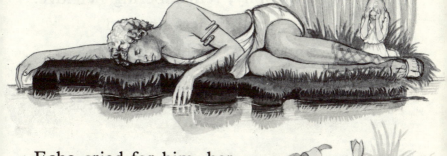

Echo cried for him, her
tears falling on the spot
where Narcissus had
been sitting.
From that place there
grew a tiny green
shoot, which slowly
became a lovely tall plant.

In spring it had white and golden flowers with a beautiful scent.

When the soft breezes blew, the flowers bent their heads, as if they were looking at their own reflections in the pool.

That plant was the first narcissus.

But Echo still wanders unhappily, remembering her love. The spell lingers on, and sometimes, if she is near by, you too may hear her sadly repeating your last few words.

The Flying Horse

When Prince Bellerophon fell in love
with Princess Philonoe of Lycia,
he asked her father for her hand
in marriage.

But the King of Lycia did not
like Prince Bellerophon very much,
and he did not want him
to marry the princess.
He thought of a plan,
then he said,

"First you will have to kill
the monster that lives
in our mountains."
He knew that people who went
to kill the monster never came back.

"What is the monster like?"
asked Bellerophon.

"It has a serpent's tail,
a goat's body and a lion's head
that breathes out fire."

When he heard this, Prince
Bellerophon was frightened,
but he still wanted to marry
the princess.

So he went to see a wise man.

"How can I kill the monster?"
he asked.

"You will first have to catch
Pegasus, the flying horse,"
said the wise man. "Then you
will be able to get near
the monster because you can only
kill it from above."

"But how can I catch Pegasus?"
asked the prince.

"You must get a golden rope,
then go to a pool called
the Horse's Well. The flying horse
drinks there every morning.
Wait there and catch him
as he drinks, with the golden rope."

Bellerophon thanked the wise man,
then went to get the rope.

With the golden rope in
his hand, he set off to find the
Horse's Well.

At last he found it at the
top of a mountain, and waited
through the night until
the sun began to rise.

As the first rays of sunlight
grew stronger, Bellerophon
saw a great white horse flying
through the sky.

Pegasus flew down to the water
and began to drink.   The prince
crept softly forward,
slipped the golden rope
round Pegasus' neck, and
jumped on his back.

Pegasus gave a great leap,
then he unfolded his wings
and flew high into the air
with Bellerophon on his back.

At first the prince was frightened,
but soon he began to enjoy flying.

They flew to the mountains
of Lycia—and there was the
monster, breathing fire and smoke!

Pegasus flew round and round it,
until at last Bellerophon
was able to kill it.

Then he went to see the king.

"I've killed the monster,"
he said. "Now may I marry
your daughter?"

But the king still did not
want him to marry Philonoe.
He said cunningly,

"First you must stop the
Amazon army which is coming
to attack my country."

The Amazons were fierce women
who went to war like men, and
everyone was frightened of them.

Bellerophon knew that Pegasus
would help him, and
he thought of a plan.

He went to a stream where
he picked up a lot of big stones.
Then he climbed on Pegasus' back
and they flew high in the sky.

When he saw the Amazon army,
Bellerophon dropped all the stones
and nearly all the Amazon women
were killed.   The others ran home.

Bellerophon went back to the king.

"I've stopped the Amazon army,"
he said.   "*Now* may I marry
your daughter?"

"You must do one more task,"
said the king, who still did
not want Bellerophon to marry
Princess Philonoe.

"Pirates are coming to attack
my country.   You must stop them."

Bellerophon knew what to do.
He flew on Pegasus high over
the pirate ships, and he
dropped great rocks on them.
The rocks fell right through
the ships, which sank,
and all the pirates drowned.

So Bellerophon married
Princess Philonoe, and they
lived happily for many years.

But Bellerophon grew
very proud, so proud that
he began to think he was
just as great as the gods
themselves.

One day he climbed on Pegasus
and set out for Olympus,
the home of the gods.

The gods were angry with him
because he was so proud,
and Zeus sent a gadfly
which stung Pegasus
so that he tipped Bellerophon off.

Bellerophon fell to the earth
below and was killed.

Pegasus went on to Olympus
and lived there for the rest
of his life.

When he died, in memory
of his great bravery, Zeus
set the winged horse amongst
the stars, so that we can
still see Pegasus in the night sky.

The Oak Tree and the Lime Tree

Zeus and Hermes were two of the greatest Greek gods, and they loved to travel in the world of men and women.

They often went in disguise so that no one would know who they were.

Late one afternoon, when they were travelling thus, they came to a small cottage where an old man and his wife lived.

The old couple were very poor.
The only clothes which they had
were the ones they were wearing,
and inside the cottage
there was only a bed,
a table and a bench to sit on.

"This is the first cottage
we have seen for many hours,"
said Zeus, when the old man
came to the door. "May we
rest here for a while?"

Now the old man and his wife
were very kind people, even
though they were so poor.
They saw that the travellers
looked very tired.

"Come in and have a meal,"
said the old man, opening
the cottage door wide.
It was so small that Zeus
and Hermes had to bend their heads
to get into the cottage.

"Do sit down," said the old

woman, pushing the bench
forward, while her husband put
some wood on the fire.

"Have you travelled far?"
asked the old man.

"We have come a long way
today," nodded Hermes.

"Then we must find you
some food," cried the old woman.

The old man went into his garden
and gathered some vegetables
and herbs, and his wife set
a pot of water on the fire.

When her husband came back, she peeled the vegetables and cut them up. Then she cut some meat from a side of ham, and put it in the pot, along with the vegetables.

While his wife was getting supper ready, the old man heated some more water, and took it to their guests.

"Here's some warm water, so that you may wash," he said.

Zeus was pleased. "Thank you," he said. "It's very welcome after such a long journey."

When the food was ready, it was set upon the table with a jug of wine and some figs from the tree in the garden.

Of course, if the old people had been by themselves, they would not have eaten so much, because they were very poor indeed.

They were so kind that they had
given their guests all the
food in the house.

The wine jug held only four
cupfuls. When the old man
had filled all the cups, the
jug was empty. Zeus drank his
quickly, then asked for more.

The old man was unhappy,
for he knew there was no more.
He looked into the jug to see
if there was perhaps a little left.
And it was full!

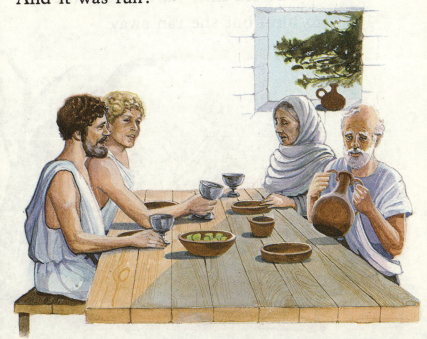

The old man looked at his wife,
then back at the jug.
When his wife looked too
and saw that the wine jug was
full, she was frightened.

"These men must be gods,"
the old man whispered to her.

"We must give them something
better to eat," she whispered back.

The only other thing they had
was an old goose. They would
cook it for these gods.

The old man called the goose
to him, but she ran away.

She seemed to know why he was
calling her, and she did not
want to be a meal for anyone,
not even the gods!

No matter how they tried,
the old man and his wife could
not catch her.

At last she ran to hide
behind Zeus and Hermes.

"Do not kill the goose," said Zeus.
"We have eaten well, and we
don't need any more."

"That was an excellent meal,"
agreed Hermes. "Now we would
like to do something for you
in exchange."

"Yes," said Zeus. "You were
kind to us before you knew
we were gods. You may have
one wish. What would you like?"

The old man and the old woman
looked at each other, then
talked quietly together.

"We have only one wish,"
said the old man at last.
"I love my wife and she loves me,
and we have never been angry
with each other.
Although we are poor, we have
always been happy, and we have
always been together.
We should like to be together
for ever, and never be parted."

"You will have your wish,"
said Zeus, and he went on his
way with Hermes.

The old man and the old woman
lived for many years.

Then one morning, when they
were very old, Zeus came by.
He saw that they could not
live much longer, so he
cast a magic spell,
and the old man and his wife
were changed into an oak tree
and a lime tree.

From that time onwards,
the trees stood side by side.
Their branches touched, and
their leaves whispered together
in the soft wind,
because once, long ago,
an old man and his wife had
been kind to the gods.

Building the Castle Wall

In a wild cold land, a long way
north of the warm and sunny land
of Greece, lived the Norsemen.

Life was not easy for them.
Snow-capped mountains covered
much of the countryside,
so that the people could
only live on the narrow plains
beside the sea.

The Norsemen loved adventure,
however, and the stories they told about
their gods were always stories of
adventure, magic and brave deeds.

The Norse gods lived in
a secret place called Asgard,
far from the homes of people.
All the gods lived there:
the great god Odin, the all-seeing one,
Thor, the god of thunder,
Loki the sly and cunning one,
and many more.

They built themselves a fine castle,
with tall towers from which they could
see all over the land.

When the castle was finished,
the great god Odin said to his son Thor,

"We must have a high wall built
around the castle grounds."

"The wall will have to be very
thick as well as high," said Thor.

"I agree with you," said Loki,
"but it will take us years to build
such a wall."

For a long time they talked about
building the wall, but nothing was done.

Then one day while they were
talking, a stranger came to them.
He was dressed like a workman,
and with him he had an old horse.

"I'll build a wall for you," he said.
"I'll build you a wall so high that
no giant will be able to get into
your castle."

The gods looked at the stranger.
Could he really build the wall, or was
he just boasting?

"How long will it take you to build
such a wall?" asked Odin.

"It will take me three years,"
said the man.

"And how much will you charge us
for building it?" asked Thor.

"I shall want three things,"
said the man. "I shall want the sun
and the moon."

Thor looked at the man who wanted

such strange things.

"That's only two things," he said.
"What's the third thing you want?"

"The third thing is this," replied
the man. "I want to marry the
goddess Freyja."

Thor could not believe his ears.

"That's impossible!" he shouted.
"You cannot marry Freyja."

"All right then," said the man.
"I won't build your wall."

He gathered up the reins of his horse
and began to move away.

Now, while Thor had been shouting
at the man, Loki had been thinking.
He had thought of a way to trick
the stranger—and Loki liked playing
tricks on people.

Quietly he spoke to the other gods.

"Let's tell the man that if he can
build the wall in one year,
working by himself, we will
give him the sun and the moon,
and he can marry Freyja."

"No!" Thor shouted again.
"He can't marry Freyja."

"It's all right," said Loki.
"No matter how hard he works, he will
only be able to build part of the wall
in a year. At the end of the year,
we will just send him away."

"Yes, that's a good idea," thought
Thor. "The man will have nothing,
and we'll have part of our wall,
which we can finish building."

"Loki, you are very cunning," said Odin.

They called the man back, and Loki
spoke to him.

"If you can build the wall in one
year, working by yourself, we will give
you the three things you ask for.
You can have the sun and the moon,
and you can marry Freyja."

"Very well," said the man.
"But if I'm to build the wall in only
a year, I'll need my horse to help me."

The gods agreed, but they did not
know that his horse was a magic horse!

The next day the man set to work.
All the gods went to watch him.

Freyja went with them, and she was very upset. She certainly did *not* want to marry this strange man.

"Don't worry," said Loki. "You won't have to marry him. No one could build a wall like that in *three* years, and in order to marry you, he has to finish it in one year."

Loki was sure that the man could not build the wall in one year—but that was before he had seen him at work.

All day long and all night long, the man and his horse worked and worked and worked.

Each day the wall grew higher and longer.

Still Loki was not worried.

"They'll soon get tired," he said.

But they did not get tired.
Day after day, and night after night,
the man and his horse worked
without stopping.

Each day the wall grew higher
and higher, and each day the wall
grew longer and longer.

The gods were getting worried,
and Freyja was afraid she might have
to marry the stranger after all.
Thor was worried too.

"What will we do when he has the sun
and the moon?" he asked. "Without

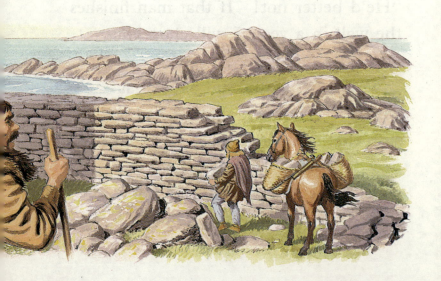

the sun and the moon, we will have no light."

"And what about Freyja?" asked Odin. "We can't let her marry that man."

He called Loki, who came quickly, for he too wondered what was going to happen.

"Well?" asked Odin. "What are we going to do?"

Loki shook his head. He did not know, but he said,

"Perhaps he won't build the wall in time. Perhaps he won't be able to finish it."

"He'd better not!" shouted Odin. "He'd better not! If that man finishes the wall in a year, I will chop you into little pieces!"

Now Loki was afraid as well as worried. He knew that he had to stop the man—and there were only two days left. How was he going to trick the stranger and his horse?

That evening the man and his horse
went to fetch some more stones.
As they were walking through
the woods, they saw another horse.
She was small and beautiful,
and she called to the man's horse.

The man's horse tried to follow this
beautiful stranger, but its master held
on to the reins.

The horse pulled the man off his feet,
and he let go of the reins as he fell
down. Now the horse was free.
The man ran after it to try to catch it.
All night long he ran after the two
horses, but he had no luck.
That night, no work was done.

Now there was only one day left
to finish the wall.   That day, the man
worked harder than ever before,
but in the evening the gods were happy.

When the sun went down, the year had
ended and their wall was not finished.

The stranger was angry.

"You tricked me!" he shouted
at Thor.   "You stole my horse!"

"*I* didn't steal your horse," said Thor.

"Neither did I," added Odin.

The man was very angry indeed, and as
he went away the gods could hear him
shouting long after he disappeared
from sight.

Thor and Odin looked at each other.
The beautiful little horse had saved
them—but how?

Then the little horse appeared before
them.   As they looked, it changed shape,
and there in front of them was Loki!
He had been the beautiful little
horse, and his trick had saved them.

Thor the Bride

Thor, the god of thunder, awoke
one morning and put out his hand.
Then he sat up in bed and
looked around.

His hammer had gone!

"My hammer! Where's my hammer?"
he shouted.

He looked in the bed, under
the bed and all around the room.

"Where's my hammer?" he shouted
again. "I must have my hammer!"

He was so angry that his red beard
stood out and his hair stood
straight up.

"Loki!" he shouted. "Have *you*
taken my hammer? Is this one
of *your* tricks?"

"No, no, no," said Loki.
"I haven't taken your hammer.
I wouldn't take it, because without
your hammer, the giants could beat us.
I'll help you to look for it."

They both looked all over the place,
but it was nowhere to be seen.

"Let's go to Freyja and ask her
to help," said Loki.

"How can she help?" asked Thor.

"She has a magic cloak made of
feathers. With the cloak, I shall
be able to fly all over the earth
until I find the hammer," said Loki.

Freyja let Loki have the magic cloak,
and soon he was flying high above
the earth.

As he flew over the mountains, Loki saw the Lord of the Giants with his horses and dogs.

"What are you doing here?" asked the Lord of the Giants.

"I'm looking for Thor's hammer," replied Loki. "Have you seen it?"

"Yes!" said the Lord of the Giants. "I took it, and I've hidden it deep down under the earth, where Thor can never find it. He can only have it back if the beautiful Freyja will promise to be my bride."

Sadly Loki flew back to Thor and told him what the Lord of the Giants had said.

"Then we must send Freyja to him," said Thor.

And so they went to see Freyja.

"Get ready, Freyja," said Thor. "You are going to marry the Lord of the Giants."

"No, I won't," said Freyja.
Then she shouted, "I *won't*!"
And her voice shook the castle.

All the other gods came to see
why Freyja was shouting, and Loki
told them what had happened.

One of the gods turned to Thor
and said,

"Since it's your hammer,
why don't *you* go to the Lord of
the Giants, dressed as Freyja?"

"Me? Dress up in Freyja's
clothes? No, no, no! You would
all laugh at me."

"If you get your hammer back,
the giants won't laugh at you!"
said Loki.

"Never!" shouted Thor.

"Then you won't get your hammer
back," said Loki.

"I'm not going anywhere dressed
in Freyja's clothes!" said Thor.

"I'll go with you, dressed as

your maid, if it would help,"
said Loki.

Thor was quiet for a moment or two,
thinking.

"All right, I'll go,"
he said at last. "But if anyone
laughs at me, they will never
laugh again."

Freyja gave Thor a long dress
which came to his feet, and they
covered his head with a veil.

Another long dress was found for
Loki, and a veil to cover his head.

Then they set off.

From the top of a mountain,
the Lord of the Giants saw them
coming, and a great feast was
made ready.

The feast began.   Thor had walked
a long way, and he was hungry.
He ate a whole ox all by himself,
and then eight salmon.

"Why does my new wife eat so much?"
asked the Lord of the Giants.

Loki lifted his veil and said,
"Because she hasn't eaten for eight
days. She would not eat or drink
until she came to you."

Then the Lord of the Giants
wanted to kiss his new wife. He
lifted Thor's veil and saw his
red angry eyes.

"Why does she have such strange
red eyes?" he asked.

"She has red eyes because she
hasn't slept since she knew that
she was to be your wife," said Loki.

"Now I'm going to give her
a present," said the Lord of the Giants.
He sent for Thor's hammer.

"This is from me to my bride,"
he said with a smile, as he gave
it to Thor.

Thor took the hammer and roared,
"And this is from me!"

He swung the great hammer and
hit the Lord of the Giants with
all his might.

Then he pulled off his veil,
and one by one he knocked out all
the giants in the great hall,
all by himself.

Never again did the giants
try to steal his hammer.